Claudette J. Spence

Nurturing The Garden of Joy

Provocative Essays On Relationships

CSolutions
New York, NY

Library of Congress Catalog-in-Publication Data
is available from the publisher.

Spence, Claudette.
Nurturing the garden of joy:
provocative essays on relationships / Claudette Spence
ISBN 0-9760911-0-0

This book is available at special quantity discounts for bulk purchases for sales promotions, premiums, fund-raising or educational use. Special books or book excerpts can also be created to fit specific need and occasions.

For details send your inquiry or request to Special Markets, CSolutions Publishing Group, P.O. Box 570715, Whitestone, NY 11357.

FIRST EDITION

How to Contact the Author

Professional speaker and training development specialist Claudette Spence has been inspiring and informing audiences in churches, schools and universities, in the workplace and in local communities for more than twenty years. She speaks about ideas and strategies to realize one's potential by building on individual and organizational strengths. To discuss hiring her for your next conference, fund-raiser, special event, or organizational growth opportunities, contact:

Claudette Spence
CSolutions
P.O. Box 570715
Whitestone, NY 11357
phone: 718-463-0095; fax: 501-638-9808
Email: promotions@claudettespence.com
www.claudettespence.com

DEDICATION

I dedicate this book in honor of my dad
and in loving memory of my mom

ACKNOWLEDGMENTS

This book would not have happened without the wonderful support of many people.

I appreciate Patricia Boothe (PBOO WORKS) whose dedication and enthusiasm in editing a book that is both thought provoking and fun are invaluable.

So many people contributed their time, energy, talent and finances to enrich this book. I thank each of you. I am especially grateful to Rosa Ancrum, Rev. Geoffrey Black, Desmond Blaine, Pearl Brathwaite, Ron Buford, Dawn Burrowes, L.D. Clepper, Noreen L. Duncan, Ezra Gayle, Dr. Clover Hall, Rev. Stephen Hall, Val Hernandez, Cathy Hughes, Dewet Innis, Vera Innis, Dr. Tom Kitts, Lolita Long, Louise Manigault, Dr. Monica Martin, Bishop Sidley Mullings, Heman Patel, Dr. Howard Rice, Devereaux Ricketts, Rev. Dr. Henry Simmons, Dr. Alan Small, Verna Smith, Rudolph Thompson, Patricia Titley, Virginia Turner, and WRKS-FM for providing unsurpassable inspiration during its Black History Month programming that propelled me into creatively publishing this work.

To Stan Taylor for the design concept and other invaluable ideas, to Alan Barnett for typesetting and production, and to Abram Hall for his production consultation services, I say thank you.

I remain pleasantly surprised by and thankful for the great number of people who have committed to distributing and promoting this book. I thank you for your encouragement.

And in all these experiences, I acknowledge and say *to God be the glory.*

CONTENTS

A GIFT FOR YOU

Value of the Unseen

We like to receive things. We like to receive things we can see and touch. Because of this we have a very difficult time recognizing and therefore appreciating gifts that are not tangible. The gift of an idea of how we may realize a goal or a dream is a valuable resource. The gift of encouragement and support is equally nourishing. The gift of experiencing each other while creating memorable moments brings joy to the soul. These gifts, given by those who may not be in a position to give a tangible gift, or those who recognize the value of the intangible, come with love and concern for the receiver's well being. Should we reject or minimize these gifts? I think not. Our ability to accept these concept gifts and experience gifts prepares us to accept the intangible gifts that our Creator gives us daily. These gifts while innumerable and unending certainly include forgiveness, love and acceptance of self and others, life, happiness, and joy.

WE KNOW WHEN WE KNOW!

Some of us have never dared to dream

The excitement and joy about being a woman comes from our special ability to convey love, joy, hope, faith and intuition, and embrace and affirm all life through our presence and our spirit. This is a gift that comes from our Creator. The extent to which we recognize, acknowledge and give thanks for this gift is directly related to how positively we view ourselves and life, and how fulfilled we are both personally and professionally.

Our ability to nourish the relationship between our Creator and ourselves is the foundation on which we anchor our dreams, hopes, aspirations, deeds and forgiveness of self. We experience joy in the manifestation of the dream while remembering the Source that fills us with the intrigue of being a woman. Is our time consistently spent in giving thanks for life—asking for guidance in developing a vision and plan for our lives, for the strength to make wise choices as we live the vision and the plan and for the courage to regroup when our choices are unwise?

Some of us have never dared to dream. Others have been discouraged from dreaming. Yet others have been distracted from living our dreams. Some of us have dreamed without moving to the next level of planning the plan. Maybe it's because we don't know how. But ask the question. "God, how do I go from here? How do I do that which is to the glory of you?"

For many of us, our ancestors are also an integral and important factor in our lives. The relationship developed with ancestors

brings truths, wisdom, insight and knowledge that women over the ages have enjoyed.

Many women have no doubt been asked, in the absence of evidence, “How do you know that?” *We know when we know.* Call it a special privilege. When communication with Life is open and consistent, we enjoy the privilege.

Wherever you are in the process of life, be encouraged that the time is now to create your dream, develop your plan, consistently live the plan, continuously give the Creator thanks for the resources that come into your lives to make the plan a reality, and intentionally keep open dialogue with the Creator.

THE POWER OF "NO"

Get ready for some people to call you selfish

Women have a hard time saying "no" and holding to that response. We avoid saying "no" because we want to be liked by everybody. But consider this: Why say "yes", then (1) worry about how to fulfill the commitment, (2) feel guilty or ashamed about carrying out the commitment, or (3) not follow through on what you agreed to do. The energy we expend as a result of these scenarios can be much more wisely spent. Consider, for example using this energy to do something you really enjoy that is good for you. Consider using this energy in active pursuit of your life's mission (which I hope is not "to please everybody with your compliance to their every wish").

Saying "no" is powerful! Saying "no" to an excessive or unreasonable demand on your time, talent and other resources is healthy for you. Reclaim your time for yourself. Visualize your life, plan it, implement it, check and recheck on your progress and include saying "no" to those things that you really do not want to do. Saying "no" is an honorable response. It is far more honorable than saying "yes" and not fulfilling your commitment.

When you are clear that you want to say "no", be assertive with it. If you are new to saying "no", folks may try to intimidate you into changing your mind. Practice an assertive "no". It is simple and direct. "No, I am not able to help you with that." If the relationship is one where you think it warrants an explanation, then, you may say, "No, I am not able to do that because it conflicts with my values, . . . I have another commitment, . . . It's not of interest to me." Ensure that your nonverbal actions are also assertive.

Make sure your voice is firm, and if you are in a face-to-face dialogue, look into the person's eyes as you give your response.

Remember, when someone makes a request of you, it is okay to ask for time to think it over. And in thinking the request over, keep in mind that the decision is entirely yours.

If you are saying "no" to someone whom you would help under different circumstances, you may explain that you are not able to help at this time. Go on to say that if she still requires your help you can be available at a specific date and time. For example: "I'm not able to baby-sit for you this weekend. I am available next weekend. If you need my help then, let me know by Thursday." If she doesn't let you know by Thursday, do not feel obligated to keep your weekend open waiting for her response. If she calls Friday or Saturday, and if you have made other arrangements for your weekend, do not hesitate to say, "Sorry, I can't help you. When I did not hear from you on Thursday, as we agreed, I made other arrangements for the weekend." No need for you to feel guilty for saying "no" here. You acted responsibly and assertively.

Then get ready for some people to call you cold and selfish. Don't be swayed by that. You're taking back control of your life and they don't like that. You will like yourself better and that is what is important.

PUT A LIMIT ON HUMILITY

Shyness begins to fade

Some of us find it difficult to "talk about ourselves." In the workplace, this translates to our coworkers and supervisors as shyness. Shyness in the workplace can limit our opportunities for professional growth.

Talking about what we do professionally or what we have accomplished professionally is a statement of fact. From such dialogue, others understand the skill, experience, and maybe the compassion we bring to the relationship. Talking about what we are doing and have done professionally is not boasting, if not done in a boastful manner.

Talking about what we have accomplished is a way to acknowledge our sense of having made a contribution to the lives of others and to recognize that our efforts bear fruits. It builds our confidence and prepares us to meet the upcoming challenge with a winning attitude.

Some women are reluctant to publicly acknowledge their accomplishments and contributions to their families and to society at-large! Why? We may have learned that "self praise is no recommendation." We are advised to allow others to speak about us or that our good deeds will speak for us. Indeed our good deeds will speak for us! And we must speak for ourselves! Probably, it is the fear of being judged by others that stops us from affirming our accomplishments. But guess what? We are being judged anyway. So we may as well place the facts on the table and position ourselves to grow with the wonderful opportunities that will come to us as a result of that affirmation.

It has been my experience through facilitating human resource training sessions that employees do not give themselves credit for all they have accomplished. They focus primarily on what they have not accomplished and use that as their benchmark for non-success. With my cajoling, they begin to be more honest with themselves, then realize the many ways in which they have already achieved success. With this insight they move toward being less harsh on themselves and more affirming of their lives.

Once they begin to see and articulate what they have accomplished, the shyness begins to fade. With improved communication skills and renewed confidence, women (and men) not only become more comfortable talking about their accomplishments, but also begin to see and express their dreams and goals. Soon, talking about themselves is no longer a laborious experience.

Women who grew up accepting the value of humility need to be reminded that being humble does not mean withholding the facts about their professional contributions. It does mean that you do so in the appropriate time and environment. It does mean that you acknowledge the Greater Source that allows you to achieve, and that you remain mindful and thankful for all God's gifts.

NO WRETCH HERE

We are worthy

The things we believe and say about ourselves come back to us in many ways. Therefore, we ought to be mindful of what we say about ourselves, even in jest, especially if it can be perceived as being unpleasant, discouraging or negative. Sooner or later these thoughts become self-fulfilling prophecies and affect our sense of worth. Initially, we may disagree with this assessment but on closer scrutiny, we realize that the "negative" things we say about ourselves reflect in the way we treat ourselves, the way others treat us, and our acceptance of that treatment.

Although we may exhibit secular signs of outward success—like the acquisition of car, home, education, children, good income, marriage (the quality of the marriage relationship is never a barometer for success!)—some part of our spirit may be broken. We are unable to look people in the eye when we speak with them. We take on a timid approach to conversations. Or we take on a boisterous, aggressive demeanor to camouflage our perceived and self-imposed lack of worth.

There is a popular song, often sung on Sundays by Christians that has lyrics, which include, "Amazing grace, how sweet the sound that saved a wretch like me." I don't sing that anymore, since I am convinced that I am no wretch. And neither are you! Examine the songs you've been singing for years to see which lyrics reinforce negative images of you.

These Christian and other religious songs may not be the only source of internalized negative self images. Family members, often in ignorance, feed us negatives. Think of an adult who, while smiling, calls a child ugly. Do you think this child will grow

up thinking she is ugly? What unwise choices must have been made based on this image of self!

How do we subconsciously project our sense of unworthiness? There are numerous ways in which we do that in our homes and social and professional relationships. It's time to examine ourselves and ask: "Who am I?" "How can I let my light shine?" A favorite Sunday School song comes to mind, "This little light of mine, I'm gonna let it shine; this little light of mine, I'm gonna let it shine; this little light of mine, I'm gonna let it shine, let it shine, let it shine, let it shine!"

We are worthy. We are worthy irrespective of the errors and mistakes we make. So let us say good, positive things about ourselves. Not boastful or pompous things, but honest, as we strive to grow in truth and grace. The good we believe and say about ourselves will enrich us in many, unexpected, delightful ways. Let our light shine!

HOW TO CHOOSE BEFORE GIVING YOUR LOVE

Treat your self the way you want to be treated

It is important to remember that our Creator loves us. Our Creator loves us regardless of height, weight, complexion, hair texture, sexual orientation or character shortcomings. Armed with the confidence of that knowledge, we grow to love ourselves, especially as we recognize our character shortcomings and work at adjusting them into healthy assets. This ability to correct our flaws brings with it a fulfillment that translates into a healthy appreciation of self. As we make these character adjustments, our love of self manifests in numerous ways and the joy that flows from that becomes contagious. As a result, we attract and nurture relationships that are healthy for our lives.

As we grow in the understanding of ourselves and our relationships, the following self-fulfilling prophecy manifests itself: *I believe I am important; I have a self-perception that I want to be treated special by my behavior; I make my wants known, and the result is that others treat me special.* If we believe these things and act accordingly, we will be sure to get results.

By our behavior, we make our wants known. Treat yourself the way you want to be treated. Do not hesitate to tell anyone who you think will be supportive what you want out of life. And how do you know that Mr. Right is Mr. Right? You must know what is important to you and how you want to be treated. Do you want to be in a relationship with someone who is interested in developing his spiritual life? Do you want someone who takes care of

himself? Do you want someone who demonstrates that he is committed to the relationship and is willing to work at it? Do you want someone who has a strong sense of integrity and fidelity? And what does that mean to each of you? Do not be reluctant to put together, for yourself, the important qualities you would like your mate to bring to the relationship. And, to be fair, ask for qualities that you bring to the relationship. Know what qualities you can peacefully live with, and also know what are definite things you will not tolerate. Spend quality time with yourself getting clear on what it is that you want.

Now you are attracted to a friend, or he to you. Observe the patterns of his behavior. Be honest with yourself about what he brings to your relationship. Remember, you get to choose. You choose to be in a relationship with him because he confirms your self-fulfilling prophecy. You can also choose to change the nature of the relationship if he is not healthy for you. Choose him because he also brings with him the qualities you believe to be important to you and your relationship, and his growing areas are not an issue to you. Choose him, treat him special, and enjoy.

IS HE LIKELY TO BE ABUSIVE—SOME EARLY WARNING SIGNS

It is your choice

We choose our relationships. We can choose not to be in an abusive relationship. And our ability to choose our partners wisely depends on several factors. Let us examine some predictors that will increase our awareness as to whether our intended partner is predisposed to being abusive.

Does he have strong "traditional" ideas about what a man should be and what a woman should be? Does he think that when you converse with him and offer perspectives different from his you are challenging his manhood? Is he jealous of your other relationships—not just with other men but also with your women friends and your family? Does he want to know where you are all the time? Does he become angry if you do not fulfill his wishes or if you cannot anticipate what he wants? Does he go through extreme highs and lows—almost as if he were two different people? Is he extremely cruel one time, and extremely kind the next? Does he physically force you to do things you do not want to do? Did he grow up in a violent home? Does he abuse alcohol or other drugs? Does he tend to use force or violence to "solve" his problems? Does he have a quick temper? Does he over-react to little problems?

These are some of the behavior patterns we must be aware of as we begin to develop close ties with those whom we want to share our intimate and family lives. There is no need to fall blindly into a relationship. It is your choice. Prepare a checklist for the behav-

iors you do not want in your life. Prepare one too for beliefs and behaviors you do want to enjoy. You may believe, quite strongly, that it is much healthier for you to not be in an intimate adult relationship than to be in an abusive one. Remember, it is your choice.

Examine the behavior of a potential mate before choosing to commit yourself emotionally to the relationship. Once you are in an abusive relationship, it can be very difficult and painful to extricate yourself from it. But you must leave it.

And do not make the mistake in believing that abusive behavior unfolds only in heterosexual relationships. All intimate relationships are fertile ground for abuse. Be alert!

INDEPENDENT WOMAN

Our state of being is wonderful

Women, be aware of men who say they want to be in a long-term relationship with an independent woman!

Many of us have worked diligently at preparing ourselves for a better life. We have expanded our horizons in many ways. We have gained knowledge from a formal education system. We have developed skills in the workplace and at professional schools. We have kept ourselves abreast of current and global affairs. We have sought ways to expand our minds, body, soul and the material comforts we enjoy. We make decisions for ourselves and live through, without complaint and anger, the consequences of those decisions. We seek the counsel and support of progressive-minded people. We envision and plan our lives. We are emotionally stable, financially capable, physically fit and spiritually growing. We are supporting ourselves in our journey to be self-supporting and self-sufficient—we are independent!

For many of us our state of being is wonderful. And we seek a mate with whom to share our love and our independent self; someone who can appreciate the independent woman that we are. Then, along comes a man who says he wants to be with an independent woman. As the relationship progresses, we realize that each party has a different definition of independent. We soon realize that for him an independent woman is not one who can initiate and carry on an intelligent conversation. She is not one who can argue philosophically with an opposing point of view—one different from his. She is not one who can articulate that which she desires for her life and is willing to invest her time and resources in the pursuit of that.

His definition of an independent woman far too frequently is one who brings her own money to the relationship to support herself so he does not have to take on any part of that financial responsibility. Sometimes, he even wants her to financially support him.

We have invested several years growing to be self-supporting and enduring, and learning from the pain and enjoying the journey. There is no need to discard all that for an insecure person whose envy of you and your accomplishments can eventually vanquish your sense of self. Step aside. Continue to enjoy your life and await the person who complements you, who appreciates who you are and with whom you share a vision of how you can be mutually supportive of each other and as a family.

THE CHOICE: WHOSE IS IT?

Life is never the same

Over one million abortions are performed in the United States each year. And while it is the woman who walks into the operating room for the procedure, and it is assumed that it is her choice, many women are urged, cajoled, and even threatened by the father-to-be to abort.

The decision to not carry a child to term is not an easy one for many women. This is especially true for those women who have been raised with the belief that women are supposed to bear children and if they do not then they are not women; that all life is sacred, so no matter what the size or shape of the fetus, it is a life to be honored and brought into this world; and that abortion is immoral and a sin.

A woman who had never been pregnant says she used to be pro-choice. When she became pregnant and experienced the bonding with her unborn child, she realized that it must be a gut-wrenching decision for a woman to terminate her pregnancy. Another woman who chose to discontinue her pregnancy tells of the guilt and sadness she experienced as she thought about the life she decided to still. Yet another speaks of the guilt she felt for having succumbed to the father-to-be's urging that she abort because he did not want this child. His urging may be considered a gentler approach than the man who tried to stomp the baby out of its mother's stomach.

What kind of man asks a woman to make this type of choice? The type of man no woman ought to be in an intimate relationship with. Remember, if he says he does not want to have children, do not walk down the path that will lead you to make some life-

changing, profound decisions for your life and that of your unborn child. Life is challenging enough without adding the burden of this insensitive man to the shopping cart.

The choice to carry the pregnancy to term or not must be solely the woman's. The physiological and emotional separation affects her in a manner different from and maybe more profound than it affects the father-to-be.

Life is never the same after choosing to have an abortion. Life is never the same after choosing to bring a child into this life. Truth is life is never the same one day to the next. However, while we are having fun, it behooves us to plan ahead so that the heart-wrenching choice of "to have" or "not to have" is a non-issue. And should you decide to be a pro-choicer, it is important to speak with health care professionals to gain knowledge and understanding on your options, and to receive mental health and spiritual counseling that together help to support and guide you in making the right and best choice for you.

MORE THAN ONE

An approach to creating an honest relationship

We often hear heartbreaking stories of women who suffer through relationships with cheating mates. And many of us are no doubt familiar with advice columns that warn against entering into intimate relationships with married men. Some of us heed that advice, yet others do not.

A recent Divorce Court episode had me in stitches. The husband/defendant explained to the judge that he had several women and that his wife was aware of his behavior and belief for the eight years before they were married and for the two years of their marriage. He posited that there were more women than men in the world and because he was kind, loving and a provider for others and for his wife she should be happy. Once she started being unhappy with him, he felt obligated to refrain from coming home and to spend more time with his other women.

I was impressed with his honesty. He had told his wife, at the time of their meeting and during their courtship, of his belief against monogamy. He lived his life based on his belief before and after they were married.

She was a fortunate woman. Her mate was honest with her. Many of us who desire monogamy never state it; we fool ourselves into thinking that a philandering man will change because of us. This is unfortunate, because this unmet expectation brings emotional pain.

While both parties to a deceptive relationship share responsibility for their actions, I would like to ask women to try diligently to not participate in relationships that they know will cause pain

to the wife of their married partners and eventually to themselves. As we move through the beginning of this new millennium, maybe we can be more supportive of our sister/women friends. If we know that a man is neither legally nor emotionally available for an intimate relationship with us, why engage him and by extension cause pain for another and eventually for ourselves?

Some may call this the high moral road. Maybe that's what it is. However, it is also an approach to creating an honest, loving, intimate, enduring, relationship that requires time and attention from both individuals—an approach that is supportive of our sisters and ourselves. It is an unselfish approach—one that asks, *What's in it for my emotional and spiritual health and that of the world of which I am a part?* Not, *What's in it for me for the moment?*

THE OTHER FOOT

We want to be treated special

A reader once asked me about a perspective I had shared in a weekly column. He wanted to know, "What does a man look for when he is choosing a woman?" His question was based on the article directed to women, which came at the end of a series that looked at the physical and mental violence that men inflict on women in their close relationships. The series went on to posit some behaviors that may indicate that a man would be abusive, and it ended with some ideas on how women may choose a mate, a close friendship, and develop a long-term healthy relationship.

The reader's query made me more aware that men too are challenged in their choice of women friends in their journey to develop healthy intimate relationships. I believe that understanding oneself, being non-judgmental of self and others, letting others know how you would like to be treated and acting accordingly, and treating yourself special are important factors in attracting and choosing a friend with whom you can develop a close long-term intimate friendship.

Maybe one of the things that is important here is that regardless of gender or sexual orientation, most of us really want to be treated special by someone who is close to us that we may call lover, friend, mate or family member. The affinity we have to people who treat us "special" is, I believe, a testimony to our wanting to be treated that way. However, we ought to exercise discretion in choosing the persons from whom we openly and quickly receive special treatment. We need not accept everything that comes to us as a gift. With a discerning spirit, we are able to choose that which is right for us at that time in our development. For us to say,

"Thank you, but no thank you," is an empowering experience. Too often, for example, we see young girls who get caught up in unhealthy relationships because some young or older man with ulterior motives brings some affection to her. She has not yet learned to be discerning and to choose wisely.

Whether we are man or woman, whether we are younger or older, whatever our calling, we may want to consider just being honest with ourselves about who we are, what we would like to enjoy from life, how we want to be treated and how we treat others. As we remain open and focused on our growth and development, choosing wisely can be an outcome of the process from which flows a deep-seated, peace-filled fulfillment. This approach toward fulfillment applies to all our relationships, be they personal, family, business and societal.

ENDING RELATIONSHIPS

Honestly assess. Constructively analyze

How do we begin to end a relationship? Most individuals have difficulty doing so. Whether we are ending a professional relationship or a personal one, we often end up feeling hurt. We feel as if the other party has wronged us. But is that really the case?

There are a few questions we should ask ourselves: How did we contribute to what happened? There are no victims in this picture. How did we navigate the relationship? How did we contribute to making it end? As a matter of fact, I like to look at this from a perspective that says, "The relationship doesn't end. It changes." Like life, things change. Relationships change. How do we then prepare ourselves to navigate changing relationships? First, with a belief that says change is an integral part of life. Next, we begin to prepare ourselves to accept and welcome change into our lives.

At work, we may begin to plan for these changes by realizing that our employment is one that could terminate at any time, for whatever reason. Whether it is fair or not is not the issue. What is, however, is our ability to healthily handle the change in our employment status. There is no need to blame your employer. Blaming anyone, including oneself, brings an air of negativity that allows for self-pity and lethargy. It is far more healthy and boosting to your esteem to analyze the situation. Determine the factors that led to your separation from the company. Assess the role you played and the role the company played in ending of the relationship.

Make a determination to change the habits or behaviors you exhibited in this company that allowed you to not perform at an acceptable level. Did you not communicate well enough or con-

sistently enough with your peers, colleagues and direct supervisors? Now is the time to find a way to improve your skills and communication competencies. Were you consistently late or absent from work? Lateness and absenteeism from work is often an indicator that there is a relationship that is not working well in the workplace. Is it that you are unreliable, inflexible or not open to learning new ways to perform old tasks? Is it that you are not open to new concepts and ideas?—Ideas that will allow the company to grow and become more effective at its mission and goals. What behavior patterns did you exhibit that prevented you from changing, and that allowed your employer to initiate a change in your relationship?

Now is the time to determine what type of work you really enjoy doing as you generate income to support your lifestyle. No need to be ashamed or berate yourself. Honestly assess. Constructively analyze. Determine the type of environment in which you want to work and the way you want to be treated in the workplace. Actively seek those relationships. Critically and reasonably assess which of your actions you need to change into a consistent behavior pattern.

With the joy that comes with growth, when we recognize how our own actions have limited and inhibited us, we can be thankful and appreciative of the change.

BREAST HEALTH AND WOMANHOOD

No good reason to delay

According to estimates by Women's Information Network Against Breast Cancer, breast cancer is the number one killer of American women between the ages of 35 and 54. And breast and cervical cancer will claim more than 500,000 women's lives in this decade.

Historically, women tend to delay medical care until symptoms become unbearable. Fortunately, that trend is changing. However, with the economic and financial challenges that many women face, the cost of health care, including the lack of health insurance, often prevent us from seeking medical care. The encouraging news is that the federal government provides breast and cervical cancer screening for women who are without health insurance. The Center for Disease Control's (CDC) National Breast and Cervical Cancer Early Detection Program provides this service through local facilities.

Once a woman has been tested for cancer and there are indications for treatment, the woman without health coverage faces the challenge of obtaining treatment. To address this problem, the Senate and the House passed bills S.622 and HR 4386, respectively, Breast and Cervical Cancer Prevention Treatment Act. These bills allow for medical assistance to women who have been screened through the CDC and found to have breast or cervical cancer. While this is a move in the right direction, the treatment is limited to women who are diagnosed through the CDC. And it is limited, based on its language, to only women; men with breast cancer who are without medical insurance still have to fend for themselves.

A woman basically has no good reason to not have a medical examination to detect breast or cervical cancer. Early detection and treatment remain the best defense for managing breast and cervical health and living a healthy life.

While I say no woman has a good reason for delaying a breast exam, there are those who fear—before a diagnosis—the surgical removal of the breast because breasts are linked to sexuality and womanhood. The treatments for breast cancer vary. Removal of the breast is not the only treatment. However, if you want to call this a worst case scenario where your treatment is for the removal of your breast(s), and you equate your womanhood with your breast, then you must spend some time examining your definition of self, reshaping some beliefs that inhibit your growth and caring for yourself, and determine the extent to which you allow societal definitions to limit you. Then look at how these limits deter you from getting diagnosis and treatment.

What is your definition of womanhood? For the woman who is unable to give birth, is she a woman? For the woman who has not given birth, is she a woman? For the woman who has had her breasts, ovaries, fallopian tubes, uterus or cervix surgically removed, is she a woman? Is womanhood based on the biological organs that make us different from men? For you, what is the essence of woman?

WOMEN, KEEP OUR HIV RATE LOW

Men and women—move away from denial

As women, we ought to take special note. The HIV virus is more easily transmitted from men to women. Fact. More men are infected than women. Fact.

The National Institute of Health reports that,

> "The number of women with HIV (human immunodeficiency virus) infection and AIDS (acquired immunodeficiency syndrome) has been increasing steadily worldwide. By the end of 2003, according to the World Health Organization (WHO), 19.2 million women were living with HIV/AIDS worldwide, accounting for approximately 50 percent of the 40 million adults living with HIV/AIDS.
>
> "By the end of 2002, 159,271 adolescent and adult women in the United States were reported as having AIDS. Based on cases reported to the Centers for Disease Control and Prevention (CDC) through December 2002, more than 57,376 women have been infected with HIV. Among adolescent and adult women, the proportion of AIDS cases more than tripled from 7 percent in 1985 to 26 percent in 2002. Nonetheless, AIDS cases in adolescent and adult women have declined by 17 percent and have plateaued in the past 4 years, reflecting the success of antiretroviral therapies in preventing the development of AIDS.
>
> "Worldwide, more than 90 percent of all adolescent and adult HIV infections have resulted from heterosexual intercourse. Women are particularly vulnerable to heterosexual transmission of HIV due to substantial mucosal exposure to seminal fluids.

> This biological fact amplifies the risk of HIV transmission when coupled with the high prevalence of non-consensual sex, sex without condom use, and the unknown and/or high-risk behaviors of their partners.
>
> "Older women are also increasingly being diagnosed with HIV infection. As of December 2001, women aged 45 and older accounted for 18 percent of the female AIDS cases reported to the CDC.
>
> "HIV disproportionately affects African-American and Hispanic women. Together they represent less than 25 percent of all U.S. women, yet they account for more than 82 percent of AIDS cases in women." (www.niaid.nih.gov/factsheets/womenhiv.htm)

In our culture, too many of our men live in denial of their sexual habits, as do the women. And, unfortunately, too many women are trusting of the man with whom they are having sexual relations and, consequently, refuse to insist that their partners use condoms and practice safe sex. In a (sub) culture that has promoted male promiscuity as an indicator of manhood, we want to believe that our partner is the exception to the rule. He just may be. But it is important that we take the time to examine closely his behavior and his philosophy on life and relationships. We must protect ourselves. Ask him the hard questions about his sexuality. Listen carefully. Look for inconsistencies between and among actions and words. Do not make excuses for him. If his behavior indicates, or if he honestly tells you, he is involved with others besides you, please believe him. Choose not to have sexual relations with him. Friendships without sex are fabulous and certainly healthier—mentally and physiologically. Or insist on practicing safer sex. This definitely includes the use of condoms. If he won't use a condom and you want to stay healthy, you know what your choice is, so you can remain healthy.

Women, we must take better care of ourselves. We must take greater responsibility for our lives and our choices. In this day and age of abundant information on HIV/AIDS, it is foolish to leave ourselves open to sexually transmitted diseases. Yes, we have made and will continue to make fools of ourselves in many ways. But, if we have risked our health and have been fortunate not to contract the virus that causes HIV/AIDS, then let us make a commitment to ourselves to begin today to be less foolhardy and more responsible in our behavior.

Remember HIV/AIDS knows no nationality, ethnicity, profession, social standing, education level, income level, net worth, size, shape, beauty or handsomeness of body. Let's educate ourselves, love ourselves more and act a tad more responsibly.

ARE YOU AWARE OF YOUR GYNECOLOGICAL CANCER RISK?

Yield not to fear of the unknown.
Engage in early detection practices

Age is not a prerequisite for cancer. Nor is it a prerequisite for reproductive cancer. There is a fallacy that only older, more mature women are prone to breast or gynecological cancer. Yet, women in their twenties are known to have these cancers. It is, therefore, very important for younger women to engage in early detection practices.

Gynecological cancer is the fourth most common cancer in women living in the U.S. Every year, more than 82,000 women in the U.S. are diagnosed with one of six gynecological or reproductive cancers—cervical, ovarian, uterine, vaginal, vulvar and tubal. Unfortunately, many of us are not aware that we are at risk for these potential killers and that early detection and treatment can extend and improve the quality of our lives.

The Gynecological Cancer Foundation and the Society for Gynecological Oncologists have declared September as National Cancer Awareness Month. During September many hospitals and other health care facilities step up their activities to increase awareness among women about ways to detect, prevent and treat gynecological cancers. For those who are without health insurance, there are free screenings and, in some instances, free treatment available at health care facilities.

Ladies, take time out for yourselves during the month of September—visit your gynecologist or a health care facility to learn more about your reproductive health. Whether you are in

your early reproductive years, the late ones, or somewhere in between on the maturity scale, take the time to manage your health. Yield not to fear of the unknown. Should there be a problem with your reproductive organs, early detection and early treatment increase your chances of living healthier and longer lives. Remember, acting out of fear, or not being proactive because of fear, is a paralyzing experience.

Release the bondage of fear and make haste to your reputable gynecologist or health care facility, taking with you, as best you can, the reproductive cancer history of your family. Stay well!

FRUITS OF DISCIPLINE

Practice new insights

We often hear that as individuals of our community it is discipline, which we lack, that impedes the revelation of our capacity to be self-sufficient. Indeed this is so among many of us. It is an absence of discipline that stems from our inability to have a broad vision for our lives, the ignorance of what paths to take to get there and the absence of guidance from childhood on practicing behavior that builds discipline.

Witness, for example, the early effects on young and older adults who are learning management skills in community-based organizations. These skills are designed to introduce and teach adults how to be more effective in the workplace. They are designed to teach work ethics which, when applied, will assist them to be more accomplished in the workplace.

As one who writes curriculum and facilitates these training sessions, it became very clear, based on professional and personal experience, that for us to be more successful in the workplace, we have to broaden our approach from teaching job skills to teaching life skills. This experience teaches that as participants become more convinced that discipline—the consistently wise use of all our resources to accomplish our life's mission—is needed in their lives, they become less resistant and more open to learning. While one may posit several ways to achieve discipline, we often begin with asking participants to begin each day with five minutes of quiet time. During this time, we encourage them to give thanks for the day, think through what they would like to accomplish for the day, and ask their Creator for the resources to make this possible. Some ask if it is meditation or prayer. As a Christian, I call

it prayer. However, I encourage them to call it what their spiritual or religious beliefs lead them to call it. The important thing I emphasize is that this consistent daily practice begins to build a discipline that can have greater impact on our abilities to acquire the material things we want to enjoy and to help us grow to become the people we want to become.

In the brief hours of the overall training session, many participants forget to do the exercise. Invariably, there are a handful of people who are diligent in trying to practice their new insights. One woman eagerly and happily reported the effects of taking those early morning minutes to listen to herself and plan her life. Through this practice, she reported, she had the insight on how to initiate a conversation with her husband. They had been battling verbally, uncharacteristically so, with each other for a few weeks. She reported, quite passionately, that she asked her husband, "What is the problem?" Fortunately for her, he honestly identified it. As their discussion continued, they realized each had been reacting to the other based on their unspoken expectations of each other. She was ecstatic. They were on their way to resolving their conflict and she was on her way to becoming more disciplined and enjoying the fruits of that effort.

It was a fitting segue for our next lesson of introducing her and other participants to additional communication skills that when applied would help us all be more accomplished managers of our lives.

FROM UNDERACHIEVEMENT TO ACHIEVEMENT

Visibly become more confident

Women who have been absent from the workforce for several years and who are going back to work outside the home are in need of a support system that encourages them to succeed.

In order for programs like the Welfare-To-Work initiative to have an effective social and economic impact, the participants must be exposed to concepts and skills that will, if practiced regularly, improve their confidence and workplace skill level. While participants in this program are taught the technical aspects of different trades and professions, an important component remains unaddressed. The fact that some women may not see themselves as having any accomplishments or successes in life is a major obstacle to preparing them for success in the workplace.

Among the tasks of my occupation, I am a part of a team that teaches success development concepts and skills to women and to men who are re-entering the workplace. Through the facilitation of forums, we introduce participants to the tools for success and fulfillment. We work to shift paradigms that limit. We build participants' confidence, abilities and skills to achieve their dreams. Some of these participants are, for the first time, beginning to get some clarity on experiences in their lives that have challenged them. Others gain confidence in expressing their dreams for living. While others come away with insights learned from sharing in other people's experiences.

During one of our daily sessions, one of the participants shared: "My life is shot." A lecture ensued that covered what it

meant to be alive, the prosperity that comes with the absence of that attitude, and how shifting that mindset will create a better person who can be the best parent for his/her child. All participants were attentive listeners, then they engaged in discussion. One participant who had been quiet and less vocal than others shared the lesson he had learned. He had also been thinking his life was shot. He now realizes, he said, that he has a lot to live for and feels more confident moving forward. He plans to graduate high school next year and attend college in the fall.

Another participant, a young woman, said she was embarrassed because she is receiving public assistance and not working. Her challenge is to recognize what options are available to her and to map out a plan based on her dreams of achievement. As she articulated her vision of how she wanted to live, and came to realize the next steps she needed to take in accomplishing her dreams, she visibly became more confident. She later participated in group discussions and even stood in front of the group to make one of her presentations.

The feelings we have about ourselves impact our ability to achieve. They affect our success-ability. Men and women are in need of success-ability tools that will help them reach and maintain success and fulfillment. This optimistic and disciplined approach transfers over time into healthy employer/employee relations and into all other aspects of our lives.

DRESS: INAPPROPRIATE

Replace moping with hoping

There is a code of conduct that emphasizes appropriate behavior. For example, in the workplace, the only appropriate touch is that of a handshake—no hugging and kissing as in a family setting. There is also a code of conduct that emphasizes appropriate attire.

One Easter Sunday, I heard a sermon that called us to look at and adjust our inappropriate internal dress so we can be presentable to our neighbors and to God. The sermon was based on the third chapter of Colossians.

The inappropriate attire of which the pastor preached was the inner dress of rage, anger, malice, and slander. These things he urged are inhibiting and are roadblocks to our receiving the blessings of life.

He called on us to replace boasting with humility; remorse with enjoyment; coldness with warm compassion; moping with hoping; and grief with relief.

As I reflected on his message, it made sense. Most of us can recognize when an inappropriate behavior can minimize or eliminate our chance for success. Likewise, I see and know how inappropriate internal attire can limit us. It limits our awareness to God's gifts. It limits the ways in which we relate to and with our neighbors and friends, and with our God. It limits our potential to be fulfilled. Similarly, the appropriate inner attire brings joy, gentleness, compassion, forgiveness and patience.

I imagine there are other wonderful attributes that await us as we cloak our inner selves with the liberating qualities that draw us closer in relationship with our Creator, ourselves, and ultimately our neighbor.

WOMEN BOSSES ARE DIFFICULT?

We are all successful

Women as bosses in the workplace are more difficult to work for than their male counterparts. This is the sentiment of many women who report to women as supervisors and managers.

Is it the woman manager who creates the problem, or does the problem originate from the female worker who reports to her? Is the worker responsible for creating an environment for the boss to get tough and difficult?

Visualize for a moment a woman manager offering employment to another qualified woman to fill a vacancy in the workplace. This most recent employee's job performance is outstanding. The manager encourages her excellence and lauds her praise to other senior managers. As fate would have it, the most recent hire begins to understand the politics of the organization and recognizes the limited authority of her direct manager. With her strong desire to move through the ranks, the new hire systematically tries to undermine the manager who gave her the opportunity for employment.

Or imagine a woman accepting the promotion to lead an agency. Her female staff attempts to defame her credibility by telling all who will listen that the new agency head does not believe in the core programs of the agency. What propels this negative message? Would you expect the boss to be less than "difficult" in these scenarios? Maybe it is the women who are reporting to the woman boss who are the difficult ones to manage.

Women in the workplace must find ways to be supportive of their women bosses. It has been my experience that women who are not confident and secure in knowledge and understanding of themselves, justice and global issues become suspect of women who they perceive to be more successful.

The truth is we are all successful in our quests through this life. The workplace responsibilities that each of us assumes is important in the sphere of realizing the organization's and the individual's goals. The opportunity to report to a woman who is knowledgeable, progressive and fair is a benefit every woman ought to seek. To be supportive of a woman boss who respects and appreciates the assets of her staff while working with them to develop their growing areas is a chance no woman ought to miss.

So whether you are the administrative assistant, supervisor, receptionist, manager or executive manager at a company, I urge you to consider ways in which you can support your female boss. Manage your areas of responsibility in a timely manner and with a high quality of performance. Always try to make your boss "look good". The self-respecting boss will acknowledge you for your support. And even if she doesn't do it as often as you would like, you are now building your confidence in performing at or above expectation. Keep in mind that her success is your success. When you throw obstacles in her way, you hinder your growth, although there may appear to be some immediate satisfaction for your underhandedness.

Let us continue to build supportive relationships and bury the longstanding perspective that women cannot be kind and supportive of each other.

UNDERLYING ATTITUDES TOWARD WEALTH

A revealing moment

Some time ago, while engaged in self-reflection and analysis, it occurred to me that my relationship with money was rooted in a belief I had adopted during childhood.

My early religious upbringing was filled with the story of Jesus' teachings, to wit: It was better for a camel to go through the eye of a needle than for a rich man to get into heaven. That graphic image had a lasting impression on me.

I certainly wanted to get to heaven, so I was determined not to be rich. When I realized how my interpretation of this bible story had affected my desire to attract substantially more money than I was generating and that my talent and experience could command, it was a revealing moment for me.

Not only have I worked at shifting that paradigm, it is making me wonder about the (many) beliefs that we hold from our childhood and adulthood that limit us in our desire and ability to be our best. It makes me wonder how we can attract the income and other resources we would like to command to live a life that is comfortable to us.

I have come to realize that to attract, retain and share the income and other resources we desire require an attitude of thanksgiving for what we have.

Yes, I am changing my attitude toward wealth. How about you?

WOMEN MUST CHANGE THEIR ATTITUDE TOWARDS MONEY AND SO MUST EMPLOYERS

Today is a great day to start

Women are faced with special financial challenges during their working years. This also translates into hardships during the retirement years. Statistics reveal that two out of every three working women in the U.S. (approximately 73.8%) earn less than $30,000 annually; nine out of ten working women earn less than $50,000 annually; women's earnings average $0.76 for every $1.00 a man earns, representing a lifetime loss of over $300,000; and women retirees receive only half the average pension benefits that men receive.

The stark reality of financial hardships of older women in the U.S. was presented by Ms. M. Cindy Hounsell, executive director of Women's Institute for a Secure Retirement (WISER), at a forum hosted by Caribbean Women Uniting for Social and Political Action (CWUSPA) (Verna Smith, president), at Brooklyn Borough Hall [March 23, 2000], in celebration of Women's History Month. Ms. Hounsell highlighted the special challenges that compound the low income of women: 1) Women are living longer and therefore will need more retirement income, 2) women are more likely to need long-term institutional care, and 3) women with children save less because they save first for their children's education rather than for their own retirement. To underscore the latter as an unwise choice, Ms. Hounsell said, "There are no scholarships for retirement. There are scholarships for school."

How do we begin to implement a plan for our financial freedom? It is always easier to begin in our early youthful years to develop the good habits of generating income, saving and investing a portion for long- and short-term goals, spending wisely to live comfortably and giving thanks to our Creator for our gifts.

What happens if we have not developed those habits in our early formative years? Today is a great day to start on that. According to Ms. Joy Jackson, a financial specialist of The MONY Group, the first step toward achieving financial freedom and our financial goals is to change our attitude. Women must "become financially literate, plan to be rich, take informed financial risks, and not be intimidated by money. To manage money more effectively, you are to plan ahead," Ms. Jackson said.

We are to develop and live by a budget that includes savings for ourselves. This is a critical first step after a change in attitude. Think of saving as paying yourself. By the time you receive your paycheck many others have gotten paid. And there are others waiting to be paid. Include yourself at the top of the list.

During my life skills workshops, when I encourage people who are returning to the workforce "to pay themselves" first, they usually laugh at me. They say that I want them to save five dollars each week from their paychecks when the check is not enough to pay all the bills they have. At that point, I encourage them to try. It is the habit of saving that you are developing. I know it is difficult to save when the basic living bills are outstanding and overdue. However, it is in the trying that we begin to achieve.

Our hope is that this insight for all women is priceless, as it is for those who set and administer employee salaries.

A CALL FOR INTIMACY

Creating intimacy makes us vulnerable

Since the attack on the United States on September 11, 2001, there have been stories about people who are now taking the time to determine what is important to them. Invariably, the stories revolve around them now wanting to spend more time with loved ones. They say this in the context of spending less time seeking the material comforts of life.

I believe we all want to live a more comfortable life. For those of us who have grown up with or have now acquired a more comfortable life, I imagine it is much easier to spend less time acquiring and more time creating fond memories with those we love and care for. For those of us who have not acquired the financial comforts of life—ownership of home and car; ability to pay for children's schooling if public school is not an option; not having to be concerned about where your next meal is coming from; to travel for fun and recreation; to make minor and major purchases without bursting the budget; to accumulate a nest egg for immediate and future living; to embrace the expense of an active social life—we must continue to place our energies in the direction of acquiring while we balance putting in meaningful time and conversations with our loved ones.

My guess is that those of us who are just now visiting the relationships we deem important lack the communication skills necessary for creating and building intimacy. So much of our interactions are superficial. We are afraid to reveal ourselves because so many people take what we reveal as fact, weave a blanket of negativity with it and spread it around our friends and colleagues. The truth is it hurts to know that those we consider close

or our confidantes are seeking to undermine us. Yet, if we allow these experiences to limit us, we fail to step out in faith and discernment in developing trusting relationships where we begin to build intimacy.

It can be difficult to find people with whom we can share intimacies, concerns, hope, failures, joys, character flaws, and mistakes. That, however, should not prevent us from growing in sharpening our communication skills so we are able to share with those people we choose to trust the stories of our lives. Building this intimacy makes us vulnerable. Yet if we do not risk vulnerability we lose the joy of breaking the barrier to and growing a mutually healthy, important experience in our lives.

ENJOYING THE PAUSE

Different periods of fun, excitement...

They said, "You'll be sad when you turn thirty." They said the same thing when forty was approaching. They see that I haven't been sad, so now that fifty is approaching, they have not been saying anything.

The "they" of whom I speak are women friends who are older than me. Their experience with aging led them to warn me, to prepare me for the aging process. The truth is I've been sad about many things in my life, but growing older is not one of them.

I have enjoyed each phase of my life. Each had its different periods of fun, excitement, disappointments, "distractions," fulfillment, "failures," success and accomplishments. I wouldn't trade anything for the majority of them. Are there some things I would have done differently? With hindsight, as a teacher, yes! Despite that, I try not to live in the regret mode, for who can definitely play the scenario that never was? No one.

What I do want to speak to here is the phase of entering into menopause. For some of us, it is a seamless transition into a maturity that women may as well look forward to. If we are fortunate enough to live to be at that menopausal age, we can be thankful that we have now acquired a body of knowledge and wisdoms that we can pass on to our younger generation.

Our physical body also changes. Mine has. I like to say I have given up the body of a girl and taken on the body of a woman. And I love it. True there was a brief period of adjustment for me. I got accustomed to and enjoy the new-sized me.

Whether our menopausal years are induced by the surgical removal of parts of our reproductive organs, or if they are a more

natural process, we have everything to be thankful for. Life after menopause still makes us a woman with the caring, spiritual insights that contribute to make us a woman. Let's care for ourselves and enjoy a new phase of living.

OFF THE RECORD

Claim your contribution

Woman, your name may never appear in a newspaper. It may never appear in a magazine, journal or any other publication. It may never appear on the Internet. Neither will your photograph. As we celebrate Women's History Month, your name or photograph may never appear in any public relations or news publications because no one has deemed your life's contributions significant enough to warrant that exposure.

Just because no one has deemed your contributions to our society significant does not mean that you have not made your contribution and that it is not significant. Stop for a minute and think about the "small" and "grand" ways in which you have helped to make this society a better place. It is customary for women to rate themselves on the accomplishments of their children. If indeed you have *guided* children to be productive, responsible, compassionate, honest, self-supporting citizens, then claim your contribution to Women's History Month!

Whatever paid work you do, if you have made a contribution to your company in the realization of its mission—hopefully to make our society a better place—then claim your status as a contributor to Women's History Month. If you are the chief executive officer, your name and photograph may be in a publication. However, if you are a part of the support staff that helps to make the CEO and the company successful, no matter your position title, you may not have made the newspaper, but claim your contribution!

Think about the ways in which you unselfishly donate your time to charitable institutions that provide services to those who

are in need. Maybe the cause is cancer, multiple sclerosis, heart disease, diabetes, HIV/AIDS, or social, economic and political equality for women. Maybe you have taught an adult to read through an adult literacy program. Maybe you have taught a child to read. Maybe you have lent a good listening ear to someone in dire need of that attention. Who knows what the consequences may have been had you not listened. Maybe you have supported someone through withdrawal from an addiction. Claim your contribution!

There are some among you who cannot think of any contributions that you made to make society a better place. If that is indeed the case, then now is the time for you to get off the log and refocus. Today is the day to begin to ascertain what you would like to contribute to the world. Then do it.

Affirm yourself today and especially during Women's History Month as a silent, significant contributor to society. Your name and photograph may never appear in a public record for your contributions. But that's all right. You know the work you have done, and from a position of caring. The Universe knows the work you are doing. Celebrate yourself. Celebrate the women who have made it to those public records for their contributions. They have paved the way and continue to pave the way for you. Celebrate Women's History Month with confidence, sisterly camaraderie and with love!

OPTIMISM

Let's be more aware of joyous things…

Do you want to live a long healthy life? Then work to create, nurture and maintain your inner garden of love, hope, joy and optimism—all positive emotions that promote wellness.

Have you ever wondered why some people always seem so positive and upbeat? Why they appear to have no problems? It could be that their optimism fuels them to channel their energies into managing the problem, therefore, leaving them no time to bemoan, "Why me?"

Give it a try! Kick the pessimism habit and maybe good things will happen in your life: You may be out of a job or not get the job you really want. You may be without "enough" money for food or shelter. Loved ones will die. Friends, children and parents will disappoint you. You may lose money on your investments. The ones you love may not love you back or in a way you want to be loved. Your marriage or other significant intimate relationship may be heading to Splitsville. You may experience injury or illness. Life happens, but our response to life doesn't happen. We are the creators of our response. So let's create responses that promote our wellness.

Promote your optimism. Optimism does not mean that you are running around with a senseless grin on your face. It means that you recognize and understand that sad and "bad" things will happen in life; that "bad" things are isolated, temporary, and won't have a lasting effect on your life; that you don't blame yourself for everything bad that happens; or that you don't go around feeling sorry for yourself. Self-assess—honestly, analytically and with emotional maturity. Stand outside of yourself and examine with

an objective, non-judgmental eye. Believe that good things will last a long time and will have a beneficial effect on everything you do.

What you expect to happen to you in life determines your approach to pessimism or optimism and hence your wellness. Pessimism is said to be highly correlated with depression and stress, and like them, it can take a huge toll on your health.

The challenge is not to ignore the "bad" or sad things that happen in your lives. The call is for balance. Let's be more aware of the joyous things, even as we experience the sad. Let's be thankful the "bad" isn't worse. Sometimes it may seem as if it couldn't possibly be worse, but it could be! Be clear on what you would like the bright side to be, and then be diligent in your efforts to attain this realistic and reachable goal. It is helpful for your positive outlook to know what we want the bright side to be. If you don't know it, you can't work toward it, and you won't recognize it when you achieve it.

I am reminded of a woman who lost her job one week after having surgery. That job was her major source of income. Her savings dwindled over the next two years as she called on that reserve to see her through another period of inconsistent income. She continues to be optimistic about gaining financially and professionally fulfilling work. She is persistent, most times, in her pursuit. She is appreciative and thankful for all the other good and joy in her life. Her health gets better daily with her routine of meditation, exercise and regularly eating healthy foods. When money comes to her, her first expenditure is grocery shopping. Fresh fruits and vegetables and grains are a regular part of her diet. She believes it is important to take care of her health so she can pursue her other goals.

She remains optimistic that she will realize the goals she has set for herself because she now believes she is in control of her life through the help of her Creator. She takes joy from the small suc-

cesses along the way—in the full awareness and knowledge that the sum effect of "small" successes is accumulative internal satisfaction. She is nurturing her garden of love, hope, joy and optimism.

SAME GENDER UNIONS: WRONG FOCUS

Develop criteria for marriage that encourages sensible unions

It wasn't too long ago, in 2003, that the Supreme Court abolished the sodomy laws in Texas. Homophobics profess that this judicial decision coupled with the seemingly growing ubiquitous voice for and popularity of same gender relationships—more television programming featuring homosexual characterizations, and most recently a high school in New York designated for only homosexual students—will be the demise of these United States. Add this to the Episcopal church's election of Gene Robinson, who is in a same gender union, as its bishop, and if there were ever doubt that this country is on a slippery slope, this eliminates it, say those who protest same gender unions. But wait a minute. Maybe not. Our President has stepped up to the plate to make his, or is it our, position clear. He will not support same gender marriages!

I applaud President Bush's courage to speak out against a population whose collective economic and political power has gained victories for the rights of people who engage in "non-traditional" sexual unions. But who decided that marriage happens only between men and women? If two people of the same gender are caring for each other and want to legalize their commitment as a family, they ought to receive the legal benefits and responsibilities that the institution of marriage carries, if *they* so choose.

There was a time when I could not understand why same gender union couples made such a big deal out of championing for their rights. Who cares what one chooses to do within the con-

fines of consenting adulthood if it is not abusive? Why must we have "affirmative action" statements that include sexual orientation? Sexual orientation or the choice of a mate of the same gender is not something that is as easily or obviously identifiable, as are gender, race, and ethnicity, and therefore subjects those with the latter labels to discriminatory practices just by appearing on the scene.

I have come to learn that there are those among us who act, even on a suspicion that one has a preference for same-gender unions, to not only bring physical harm against such a person, but also to deny such basic rights as education, housing and employment. There are many among us who have been harassed and have been denied opportunities for growth in vital areas of life such as education, employment, promotion, access to credit and capital or affordable rates and prices for goods and services, and spiritual growth in organized religion. Why should anyone be denied these rights because she/he chooses a partner of the same gender?

Bishop Robinson's faith has brought him through life to the high profile and influential office in the church. His journey is a statement of faith, I believe. It is a statement of courage by an employer. It is a statement that regardless of one's choice of partner God wants everyone at the table of forgiveness, love, hope and life.

It is unfortunate that we have to make one's choice of a mate an issue. Or maybe we do this because it is our focus on the sex that makes us so angry and hostile. A friend who is in a heterosexual relationship concurred that to focus on people's intimate relations is no-one's buinsess. She said, "I shudder to believe that people would treat me in a manner based on what they think my husband and I do in the privacy of our bedroom!" Is that the

focus of people who dislike and maybe even fear those in a same gender union?

Yet God loves us all. And just maybe, God loves us all because God does not place the emphasis on sex or sexual "sin"—as homosexual relationships are deemed by some—as greater than, or worse than any other of our non-homosexual "sins."

Is the legalization of marriage between same gender people the next big cause to be championed? While marriage is not a fundamental right, this may be the century in which we move to set up a criteria and qualifications for marriage that encourages sensible unions. Unions between people who share a common vision for their lives together, who are compatible on sexuality, sex, work, collaborating on the creative contributions to their individual and collective growth and that of community, and where love, joy, peace, respect and timely and truthful communications within the union are mingled and tied together. A union where people honor the integrity and fidelity they cherish and care about and for each others all-around well-being.

We have focused on the wrong issue. The issue ought to be our fidelity to the principles on which the union is formed not on the gender of the partner. And if same gender partners nourish each other, then so be it.

NO MOTHERS ON MOTHER'S DAY

Attempts at a paradigm shift on motherhood

Women without children who are beyond the childbearing years view Mother's Day with varied levels of enthusiasm while at the same time many well-intentioned folks, on this and other days, encourage us to shift the paradigm of motherhood.

Encouraging folks offer to us that motherhood is not limited to birthing, but, that for us it is the loving and caring we give to children in our lives—our nieces and nephews, our godchildren, our friends' children, and even the children we may be responsible for in our professional lives as teachers, nurses, doctors, or social workers. They even extend caring to include offering a kind word or gesture to a child we do not know. While I appreciate their caring perspective, I believe it is rooted in feeling sorry for us because they think we are or were physiologically incapable of having children. It doesn't seem to occur to them that women, Black women, choose not to be parents.

I have never been asked how I feel about not having children. And the numerous women who are beyond child-bearing years, whom I interviewed, say they have never been asked that question either. People just readily feel sorry for us and begin to offer advice, or consolation: "You're the lucky one," "You can/should adopt." Or they eye you with an expression which reads "poor thing."

The women with whom I spoke had a range of feelings about not having children. For many of us who grew up in an era where the home-grown taboo of single motherhood was diminishing, we maintained the principle of raising children in the traditional

family structure of having a mother and father in the home. Our desire to have and nurture our children in a loving home with mother/father/wife/husband in a healthy relationship overrode our desire to be single parents. For many of us the desire to have children was never strong. For some it was fleeting. And for yet others it was nonexistent.

And as the childbearing years are behind us, or fast approaching, how do we manage our feelings of being childless in a society that readily celebrates and affirms motherhood? For some of us who were unequivocal about not having children that's a non-issue. For the others of us, we have moments when we feel less than woman. For example, when recently I visited the Majesty of African Motherhood art exhibit at Langston Hughes Community Library and Cultural Center, where I experienced the graphic bonding images of mother and child in sculptures from Africa, sadness engulfed me. Momentarily. Another woman said of Mother's Day, "I try to avoid Mother's Day service at church; and I still have my mother so I do something with her. And pretty soon the day is over."

For many of us the sadness does not linger. We're reconciled that we are not going to have children so to maintain our mental health wellness we've made the psychological shift to accommodate that reality. For example, a gynecologist and former obstetrician who has no children says, "I am a mother to mothers."

While I understand and admire the attempts at a paradigm shift on motherhood, I believe that to be a mother, both child and mother must reside in the same home where the mother's daily consistent influence in word and deed shapes the child's future. Anything less than that makes us a fugacious adult in a child's life.

Fulfilling Mother's Day to all!

MAN'S ROLE AS PROVIDER

Sounds grand…

A few years ago, I had a conversation with a man who said he had ended the relationship with his lady friend because she was asking other people for financial help. His view was that if they were in a relationship, then he was the man that she should be asking for financial help. Sounds like he is from the traditional school, where men expect and are expected to be the financial provider, or is it supporter, for their families. Even though they were not legally married, he had a commitment that this lady was his family. Sounds grand, but what happens when the rubber hits the road and he is not able to provide in the way which she needs? What should she do? Not seek other options and allow her financial affairs to become more complex?

While the man relating the experience shared his take on it, I queried, "Did you consider how she may have felt, knowing she had a man in her life who could not come to the plate when she was in need, and she had to seek resolve outside of the primary relationship?" "Does he really understand the issues she is experiencing, and does he really want to help?" Is it enough for him to say, "I can't help?" Does he suggest they brainstorm a strategy to resolve and improve the circumstance, or does he leave her (emotionally) alone to figure this one out?

What do you do? When you approach your family and friends in a final choice approach, you will not be surprised by the comments, directly or indirectly, by men and women, ". . . but she has a man, she has a husband." While we have made it to the 21st century, old values linger amidst the creation of new ones. Is a man a

man if he is not able to provide for his lady? Is a man's ability to provide support, financially, a criteria for manhood?

And if he is not able to provide emotional support, does that detract from his manhood?

I have been told that some men are confused about what role they want to live in a relationship. Do they want to provide emotional and financial support? If the answer is in the affirmative, how do they demonstrate this? Some want to be known as a sensitive man, because that is what women say they are looking for. If a man cannot provide emotional support and cannot provide financial support, does that make him of value to the relationship? And if he is not able to provide either, is it justifiable for the woman to seek resolution outside of the relationship—without guilt or shame? Will he accept her actions without judging her? Will his manhood be threatened?

Ladies, and gentlemen, what do you think?

ABSENTEE FATHERS

Believe men when they say they do not want to have children

Half of all children born in the U.S. today will spend half of their childhood in a family headed by a woman. Experience indicates that, among other distressing news, 90% of all homeless and runaway children, 71% of high school dropouts, and 75% of adolescent patients in chemical abuse centers are from single parent homes.

In light of these social implications, what is it that allows so many fathers to not bring time, attention, affection and money to the development of their children? One clear reason is the anger a father feels toward the mother of his child because she has entrapped him. As adults engage in adult fun, somewhere along the line the man has explicitly stated that he does not want to have children. The woman becomes a selective listener, has selective recall, or convinces herself that once she is pregnant or once the father sees the child he will change his mind about fatherhood and step up to the responsibilities. History has shown this is not the case. One wonders why women continue to act so foolishly.

Entrapping a man with a child is a surefire way to hasten the demise of a relationship and to chart your course to being the sole provider—emotionally, intellectually, financially and spiritually—for your child. And then we have the nerve to speak evil of this man when he provides minimal support or none at all!

What is a man to do when he knows he is not prepared to support a child? Once the child is here, he needs to step to the plate and make his contributions to minimize the risk of his child becoming a menace to society.

Before a child becomes a reality, the man who is clear that he does not want children must act responsibly in that regard. Abstinence or taking control for his contraceptives, for example, a vasectomy, are responsible actions to ensure he does not have children. There is no need, in these times, for a man to abdicate his responsibility for contraceptives, leaving that solely to the woman, and then cry and holler entrapment!

If we could pledge that women will believe men when they say they do not want children, that women will not entrap, that men will take responsibility for their own contraceptives, and all fathers will be supportive of their children, we can begin to strengthen areas of our families, which, if left unattended, create crises, pain and a life punctuated with hardship and misery for parents and children.

MEN ON FATHER'S DAY

Recognize those responsible men

Nowadays it's not uncommon to hear men crying about wanting equal time.

Men in heterosexual relationships want equal time, just as women have championed their causes for equality. Men want equal time when they date. They want women to treat them to dates—whether it is within the context of a committed relationship or not. They want women to anti-up the dollars to treat them the way men have traditionally courted women.

I know some women who have a hard time with that concept, because they are guided by a philosophy that says, "Men are to pay, every time, all the time." There's a word for that which many of us have come to associate with less than good. That word begins with the 16th letter of the alphabet.

Men want equality. They want the world to be aware that men who are over age thirty-five and are without children are also victims of hurtful comments from the insensitive among us. In our culture, where one popular definition of manhood is based on the number of children a man has biologically fathered, older men without children are often subjected to ridicule. Other men and women query their manhood, query their sexual orientation, or wonder about their physiological ability to procreate.

Very seldom if ever do the parochial thinkers consider that the man may have made a conscious choice to not have children because he has not yet formed a relationship with a woman whom he wants to be his partner in raising a family.

As we recognize this Father's Day, let's give recognition to those responsible men who have taken the necessary steps to ensure

that they do not bring children into one more single-parent household, where, as people of African descent living in these Americas, the child and his/her parent will have far too many unnecessary barriers placed in their lives to deter and undermine the child's success and fulfillment.

So to all the men and brothers without children who understand the awesome responsibilities of fatherhood, be encouraged that there are women and men who appreciate your perspective and actions in wanting to bring children into and creating healthy family relationships.

Happy Father's Day to all!

WOMEN ARE BETTER DRIVERS

My dad drives very differently when my mom is in the car

Throw out that longstanding myth that men are better drivers. New research indicates what women knew all along—women are safer drivers than men. And parents, when you need to find alternative transportation for your child, choose an older woman driver.

Based on a nationwide study, one of the conclusions drawn by researchers from Ford Motor Company and the University of Michigan Transportation Research Institute states, ". . . the safest drivers for children to ride with are women, especially older women." The study was based on child traffic fatality crashes in the U.S., and proposes a star rating system that assigns child injury and fatality risks according to the kind of driver who is transporting children, from infancy to age 15, in a vehicle. The study shows that women consistently rank better, that is, they pose less risk of being involved in a crash that injures or kills their minor passengers.

Older women drivers received the highest ranking for safety. The greater the difference in age between the woman driver and the child passenger, the safer the child—to a point. Women who are at least 44 years older than their passengers received the highest ranking. This usually means that grandmothers are better drivers than other family members. Parent-age women received four stars in the study. Parent-age men received three stars. When it comes to gender, male drivers are most involved in crashes that result in injuries and fatalities to child passengers. It

is reported that the researchers have overheard children remark, "My dad drives very differently when my mom is in the car."

The objective of the research was to examine real-world accident data and make specific suggestions that can help parents make decisions about whom they choose to transport their children. They found that many parents occasionally drink and drive with child passengers; that 70% of 14- and 15-year-olds killed (in auto accidents) were riding with drivers under the age of 21; and that fatalities had occurred where children between the ages of 12 and 15 were behind the wheel or were riding with young people who were, at most, only six years older.

Parents, continue to be careful and scrutinize those drivers to whom you charge your children. If you know a driver drinks, even one drink for the night, do not allow that person to drive your children. You do not know this driver's alcohol tolerance level. If the driver allows children to travel without wearing their seatbelts or without a child safety seat or allows more children into the car than the seat belts can accommodate—that's another sign of a high-risk driver. It may seem like fun to pack all the children in the back of the car, but that's a tragedy waiting to happen. For parents of teenagers, the study recommends, "Keep a list (of the young friends) who they may or may not ride with. And if your child is a teenage driver, think long and hard whether you want him or her to have passengers."

BE STUBBORN

Shed the shackle of doubt

Women have you noticed that when you are clear and insistent on doing that which you believe to be in your best interest, people—both men and women—frequently label you as stubborn? And, always, this stubbornness they project on you has a negative connotation?

Our wanting to please others, at the expense of not satisfying our true belief and calling, leaves us internally dissatisfied and less confident in our critical thinking skills and other abilities. Of course, we are aware that when a man is clear and insistent on what he wants to do, stubborn is not the word used to describe him. He is confident! He knows what he wants! He is going places!

Women, it is time we shed the shackle of doubt that creeps on us when we are called stubborn. Let's flip the script. Let us view the label stubborn as being positive—as a compliment. Stubborn implies that we are focused on that which we must do in the journey of becoming who we want to be. Stubborn implies that we have a better understanding of ourselves than those who want us to do it "their" way. Let us wrap ourselves in a sheer sheet of stubbornness.

As a matter of fact, let go of the negative connotations people apply to the many words they use to describe you. Consider the labels selfish, stubborn, picky—usually used when you are being, and rightfully so, selective in choosing a mate. I am sure there are other words you can think of that people use to deflate and chip away at your confidence.

I encourage you to be stubborn with a confidence that says: *I am in touch with me. I know who I am, what I want and what is*

pleasing to me. I have asked for guidance to choose wisely, and I am choosing wisely, with humility, gratitude and thanksgiving. I enjoy my life, and thank you very much for thinking I am stubborn, or selfish. Thanks for the compliment!

WHAT MAKES YOUR WORLD TURN?

You do

Do you ever ask, "What makes the world turn?" Or is your question, "What makes the world turn against me?"

There are those who say that to ask the former question requires time that only people with privileges have. Those who are considered to be privileged have the luxury of pondering. And those who perceive themselves as not having the material things they want from life are too busy pursuing them to have the time for query.

Just asking the question of why the world turns against me reflects a perspective that the world is against you. Just, maybe, it reflects someone who is feeling sorry for herself. Because if we were to take inventory of the privileges we have, no matter how dire our present situation may appear, we live in and with many privileges. Do you know that there are places in the world, today, where women are maimed or killed for the manner in which they dress? Where women have little, if any, voice in affairs of the home or society? Do you realize the countless privileges you now enjoy?

A student of mine once shared that she was feeling neither privileged nor successful because she had not achieved all her goals—ownership of a house and financial security and independence. Yet, as we explored the successes in her life, as we examined the present opportunities of which she was taking advantage, we realized that she was indeed privileged. She had the ability to vision and plan and was working toward achieving the material goals she had set. Yes, obstacles may delay the attainment of your

goals. But that does not translate to "underprivileged", nor does it translate to not being successful.

The world turns against you when you feel sorry for yourself. It turns against you when you are not aware of exactly what it is you want to do and what your options are for achieving your goals. It turns against you when you buy into the myth that everybody is doing better than you are. The reality is every woman has her own challenges. Every man has his own challenges. And nobody's hurdles are higher than the other. It is how we approach our obstacles that shape our attitudes and our successes. The world turns against you when you do not realize what your insecurities and unworkable beliefs and values are. The world turns against you when you turn against yourself.

What makes the world turn? You do. You make the world turn when you believe you have a contribution to make to our society. You make the world turn when you see the opportunities that life presents and act on them. You make the world turn when you learn your lessons from life and accept personal responsibility for your thoughts and actions. You make the world turn when you give thanks to the Creator for making you the privileged person that you are. You make the world turn when you take time to reflect, introspect, and query, "What makes the world turn?"

TO BE ALIVE

We are really having such a fun time…

Lately, I've been asking the question, "Why is it that so many Christians profess, 'Thank you, Jesus, for letting me see another day!'" Or, "Thank you, God, for waking me up this morning." Why are we so thankful to be alive, if as Christians we believe that on our death we will be with Jesus in eternity? It seems to me that as troublesome as this life gets, and with the promises of eternity with God as a much better deal than this one, we ought to be querying the reason we're still here.

I asked some of my brothers and sisters in my small group where we were journeying on our 40-Day Purpose spiritual growth path at my church, "Why do you give God thanks to be alive?" They convinced me that the reason we're thankful is that we have yet another day to worship God, to be a glory to God, and to be witnesses to bring unbelievers to know Jesus. That sounded so "right", I didn't have the courage to tell them I didn't believe that is the reason that many folks are thankful that they're still alive.

I think we are thankful that we're still alive because we're afraid of death. As good as or as bad as times get here, we know this life. We really do not believe in the promises of eternity. Our teachings, our experiences, our faith have not brought us to that point for us to not fear death and embrace the goodness of eternity that is promised to us.

When Jesus was preparing to be nailed to the cross, he finally said, "Thy will be done." He knew that his mission on earth was fulfilled. He had lived a God-filled life actively engaged in the

work God had placed him to do. He was ready to die because he knew also that he would live in eternity with God.

In his speech just before he was assassinated, Dr. Martin Luther King implied that he was ready to die, or he sensed his death was near. We realize that as a spiritual man, he believed he had been doing God's work and, just maybe, he knew that he had fulfilled his mission here.

What is our reason for wanting to be here? Is it that we are really having such a fun time here that we don't want to leave? Maybe we are not sure we're engaged in doing God's work, so we pray for more time here and, therefore, we are thankful for one more day. Without a strong sense that we are doing God's work and fulfilling God's mission for us, we just may fear death. Or is it that we are not sure about eternity?

What is your reason for thanking God for being alive today?

GIVING VOICE TO INFLUENCE

You have something of value to share

In a society where we've been brought up to believe that the "squeaky wheel" gets the oil, and to be loudest is to be heard, how do we begin to recognize that sometimes we're shouting so loudly that we cannot hear ourselves, and no one wants to listen to us? To speak the loudest does not mean that those who hear have listened and understood us. It means that we're so insensitive to others that we just keep on shouting, oftentimes doing what singer James Brown sang about: "Talking loud and saying nothing."

How do we move to talking softer and saying something? How do we lower the volume on our voices and articulate sparkles of wisdom that our audience will appreciate?

To give voice to your opinions, beliefs, and perspective is important. It is in the sharing that we learn and grow in understanding and sometimes in grace.

On closer examination of your speaking patterns, have you been guilty of talking loud, or talking excessively and not saying much? Loudness can be a dissonant sound. It is jarring to the ear and to the entire system. Loudness cultivates avoidance. Avoidance translates into the absence of an audience and ultimately a silenced voice.

Do you want to silence your voice? I bet not, because you believe you have something of value to share. Have you considered giving voice to your expressions not only by speaking, but also by singing, painting, writing, and meditating? Think of ways in which you may lend value to society by lowering the volume and frequency of your articulated speaking voice, and increasing your influence among us.

WHO WILL RISE TO THE CHALLENGE?

They understand the devastating implications if they remain divisive

It does not seem to abate, unfortunately. The tensions between African Americans and African Caribbeans living in the USA, and particularly where there is a high population of both groups, are not being addressed or alleviated.

The factor that is missing that will allow us to understand each other—our common history, our similarities and our differences—is rooted in a class issue. That issue is education.

It is apparent that those who have successfully navigated the college or university level, taking the time to learn about African history and the history of Africans in the Diaspora, have a clear understanding of building harmonious unifying relationships one with the other. These individuals understand the devastating implications if they remain divisive toward each other.

But only about 10% of this population attends university. That leaves a hefty 90% of both peoples initiating and perpetuating hostile relationships with each other. What a waste of time! Imagine spending that time and energy in trying to learn more about each other. Imagine spending that time building relationships that would benefit the family, the children and the African community.

Still, one of the sad results of this ignorance is that our workplace is filled with "professionals" of African descent who have earned their certificates, degrees and licenses without taking an African history course to help them understand the dynamics of

the relationships among peoples of Africa. Nor have they broadened their knowledge by taking advantage of the few community-based Africa-centered teachings. And so the majority of African descendants living in the Diaspora continue to divert their useful energy into trivial matters while propagating the universe with more negative energy than it can balance.

Is it possible that we can create a system by which we can enlighten people of African ancestry about our shared history and the benefits of building mutually satisfying relationships? Who will rise to the challenge?

REVIVAL TIME

Have we minimized our ability to feel and demonstrate compassion and justice?

As we here in the U.S. live through the impending threats of what our politicians call terrorism and the agitated state of terror alerts, it makes one wonder if our move away from organized religion is reflected in our attitude in facing the enemy and danger.

Various studies on organized religion indicate a reduction in the number of people who identify themselves as religious or who participate in organized religion. While the focus has been on the decline in the membership of the Christian church, this obvious decline may in part be that the mainline denominations have statistics which they more readily reveal than other faiths.

With that said, people are shying away from organized religion. They share various and interesting reasons for that. Here are some examples: "There are too many hypocrites there." "All they want is your money." "The pastor is . . . ." "I used to go every Sunday when I was a child." Could one implication of that response be that "I have enough religion in me to last a lifetime?" Recently this comment came to my attention, "I think the church is important, but going to church is not."

One researcher on organized religion in the U.S. said, "There does not seem to be a revival taking place in America. Whether that is measured by church attendance, born again status, or theological purity, the statistics simply do not reflect a surge of any noticeable proportions."

Could it be that in the absence of our collective struggles and growth in our spiritual lives we have minimized our ability to feel

and demonstrate compassion and justice? We need a spiritual revival in this place; in these United States!

Can we encourage the "non-religious affiliation" people to reconsider becoming a part of an organized spiritual growth institution to help us all revive the land of the free and the home of the brave?

Yes. We need a revival in this place!

HEALING IN WELLNESS INSTITUTIONS

Create a culture of wellness for employees

Our healing and development organizations, while doing some good work in some aspects of their organizational life, are in need of healing and wellness themselves. We are not talking about financial wellness. We are talking to wellness in the interpersonal relationships between and among employees.

There are 9.4 million people who are employed in health care, 2.9 million in personal care, and 1.6 million in community and social service work (U.S. Industry Outlook). These people work in institutions that are designed to heal and bring wellness to their clients.

There is a common bond among many of these institutions. They are designed for and have missions that espouse the highest ideals of wellness.

Very often these institutions are designed to meet the needs of their end-user customers. So an entity will fulfill its mission of advocacy or direct service delivery to its constituent, thereby creating a wellness environment for the end-user—usually the community resident. Faith-based institutions, churches, hospitals, spas and schools are just some of the institutions that are designed to deliver services of wellness to their consumer base. The degree to which these institutions deliver on their stated mission varies from excellent to poor. Yet among even those that deliver or approach delivering excellent service lay the haunting reality of how disrespectfully many of them treat their employees.

These wellness institutions are rife with a culture—established by their senior management—that systematically treats their employees with disrespect. This occurs in varied ways and include, but is not limited to, the tone and language used to address employees. It is not uncommon, for example, to witness people in churches speaking in harsh and hurtful words to each other and to and about their pastors. It is not uncommon for management in some of these wellness institutions to overlook, and thereby encourage, employee-to-employee conflict. It is very common for management to create an environment where communications to their employees are so untimely, and long past due, that once the information is passed along it is of little value. This is exemplified in the absence of or delay in addressing employees' performance evaluations. Managers in these wellness institutions utilize an unhealthy approach to human relations in their organizations. Many encourage and promote dysfunctional staff into management to support their chaotic and dysfunctional approach to life, which is shrouded under the organization's magnanimous missions.

The challenge for all level of managers in our healing and wellness institutions is to create a culture of wellness for their employees. They may do so by bringing wellness attitudes and behaviors into their daily work relationships with their direct reports, their co-workers and colleagues. If managers were to treat each employee with respect, regardless of his/her place on the organizational chart, regardless of his/her skin color, and regardless of his/her socio-economic status, we can begin to create a more humane relationship in the workplace and in our collective societal lives.

The managers—at all levels—of our wellness institutions need to reflect, examine and shift their attitudes and behavior toward their employees. They ought to be held accountable to create a

wellness environment for employees. A move in this direction can bring us much closer to building community.

Imagine a society where 13.0 million people in the workplace are relating with each other with dignity, respect, accuracy and timeliness of communications! Imagine a society where our workplace relationships begin to bring wellness to employees as well as to the end-user client of the products and services these institutions provide!

JOY COMES TO US

Appreciation without possession

Joy comes to us as we invite it into our lives by appreciating the beauty in everything we experience without wanting to possess it. As we see and appreciate the beauty in others, in the steaming sun, or the drizzling or pouring rain, our joy is nourished.

As we continue to see, hear, taste, feel and overall experience the beauty in all our experiences and in all our relationships, in spite of or despite that which we may call an unpleasant experience, our joy grows, as does our appreciation for our selves.

Hopefully, you can begin to compile an unending list of all the experiences that bring you and sustain your joy.

As you embrace the joy that comes to you, you will share that beauty spontaneously and effortlessly.

Give praise and glory to God.

In Joy and Grace.

EXPERIENCES THAT BRING ME JOY

List here all the experiences that bring you joy:

EXPERIENCES FOR WHICH I AM THANKFUL

List here experiences for which you are thankful:

WHAT I DREAM OF BEING

Character Traits

List here character traits, e.g., disciplined, organized, etc.:

WHAT I DREAM OF BEING

Contribution to Life

List here your goals:

WHAT I DREAM OF BEING

Relationships with Others

List here the kinds of relationships you wouuld like to have with family, friends, co-workers…:

WHAT I DREAM OF BEING

How I want to Live

List here things you can do day-to-day, week-to-week, and month-to-month to make your life more fulfilling:

RESOURCES NEEDED TO REALIZE DREAM OF BEING

Character Traits

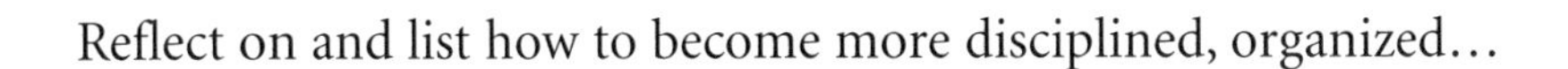

Reflect on and list how to become more disciplined, organized...

Record how you are achieving the goals above.

RESOURCES NEEDED TO REALIZE DREAM OF BEING

Contribution to Life

Reflect on and list your goals.

Record how you are achieving the goals above.

RESOURCES NEEDED TO REALIZE DREAM OF BEING

Contribution to Life

List here supportive and knowledgeable people with whom to share your ideas and who can give you some suggestions on how to proceed:

RESOURCES NEEDED TO REALIZE DREAM OF BEING

Relationships with Others

Improve communications skills:

Enroll in a class or workshop.

Read books on communications.

Contact CSolutions for communications classes:
classes@claudettespence.com

RESOURCES NEEDED TO REALIZE DREAM OF BEING

Relationships with Others

Improve negotiation skills:

Enroll in a class or workshop.

Read books on negotiations.

Contact CSolutions for negotiation classes:
classes@claudettespence.com

RESOURCES NEEDED TO REALIZE DREAM OF BEING

How I want to Live

Further your educational level:

Get a certificate, a license or a degree—whatever your interests.

Plan for above: include timelines and financial costs.

RESOURCES NEEDED TO REALIZE DREAM OF BEING

How I want to Live

Increase income:

Diversify your income streams—have more than one source of income.

Plan for above.

RESOURCES NEEDED TO REALIZE DREAM OF BEING

How I want to Live

Improve your financial literacy:

Plan for above: include reputable non-profits that offer courses.

RESOURCES NEEDED TO REALIZE DREAM OF BEING

How I want to Live

Enlist support of people with whom you have significant relationships that living your dream will affect:

List them:

Inform them.

RESOURCES NEEDED TO REALIZE DREAM OF BEING

How I want to Live

Energy:

Plan and consistently implement nutritious eating habits in consultation with your health care professional.

RESOURCES NEEDED TO REALIZE DREAM OF BEING

How I want to Live

Energy:

Plan and consistently implement an exercise routine in consultation with your health care professional.

RESOURCES NEEDED TO REALIZE DREAM OF BEING

How I want to Live

A social life:

Plan for and enjoy a social life that benefits your wellness and your joy; include at least one hobby.

RESOURCES NEEDED TO REALIZE DREAM OF BEING

How I want to Live

Meaningful work:

List the type of work you would enjoy:

Go job hunting or create your own job.

RESOURCES NEEDED TO REALIZE DREAM OF BEING

How I want to Live

Confidantes:

List names of people with whom you can talk about confidential matters:

RESOURCES NEEDED TO REALIZE DREAM OF BEING

How I want to Live

Time to evaluate, and adjust where necessary, the implementation of your plans:

How successful is the implementation of the plan?

What adjustments do you need to make to the plan? List them:

RESOURCES NEEDED TO REALIZE DREAM OF BEING

How I want to Live

Set aside time to attend to and develop your spiritual life.

ORDER FORM

Give the Gift of a Provocative Book
To Your Loved Ones—Family, Friends, Colleagues

Check your leading bookstore or order here or at www.claudettespence.com

☐ **YES,** I want ________ copies of *Nurturing The Garden of Joy: Provocative Essays on Relationships* at $12.95 each, plus $5 shipping and handling per book (New York State residents please add $1.12 sales tax per book). Overseas orders must be accompanied by postal money order in U.S. funds. Allow 10 days for delivery.

☐ **YES,** I want ________ copies on CD of *Nurturing The Garden of Joy: Provocative Essays on Relationships* at $14.95 each, plus $5 shipping and handling per CD (New York State residents please add $1.29 sales tax per CD). Overseas orders must be accompanied by postal money order in U.S. funds. Allow 10 days for delivery.

PAYMENT INFORMATION

My check or money order for $ ________________ is enclosed

Please charge my ☐ VISA ☐ MC ☐ AMEX ☐ DISCOVER

Name on Account ____

Account Number ____

Expiration Date ____

Signature ____

SHIPPING INFORMATION

Name ____

Organization ____

Address ____

City ____________________ State ________ Zip ____________

Country ____

Phone ____________________ Email ____________________

Please make your check payable and return to:

CSolutions
P.O. Box 570715
Whitestone, NY 11357
Fax: 501-638-8374

ABOUT THE AUTHOR

CLAUDETTE J. SPENCE is an Adjunct Assistant Professor of English at St. John's University in New York City. She is also a consultant for the New York Conference of the United Church of Christ, the World of Difference Project of the Anti-Defamation League, and other religious and community organizations. In addition, she has a strong background in business management and is a principal consultant at CSolutions, a corporate communications strategy and training firm. Born and raised in the Caribbean, she received her B.A. in Political Science and Communications from Queens College and her M.S. in Communications from Brooklyn College.